'Anxiety's like a rocking chair. It gives you
something to do, but it doesn't get you very far.'

JODI PICOULT

anxiety free

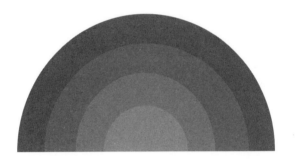

HERRON

contents

introduction **7**

understand anxiety **11**

challenge your mind **33**

regulate your body **81**

get support **109**

live your life **135**

quotes by **187**

introduction

Anxiety is a cruel master. Not only does it 'mess with our heads', it manifests in the body too, from muscle aches to heart palpitations and more, making it hard to pin down what's anxiety and what's not.

It's on the rise in the West, affecting roughly one in five people. But anxiety has been with us since the dawn of human civilisation. Those affected are not alone and never have been. Its character has changed, particularly with the advent of new technology and the pressures of social media, and we know much more about it now than ever before.

The good news is that it is possible to find a way out of anxiety's vice-like grip. It starts, like everything, with understanding. There is a reason for anxiety. Due to stress, the body's 'fight or flight' response (an animal instinct designed to prepare for predators) is in overdrive. Lion attacks are few and far between these days but our bodies don't realise. As a result, we are on high alert far beyond what the circumstance requires. Eventually, we can get stuck in this mode, and it becomes a job to retrain the body to relax. For this there are skills you can learn and practise, such as yoga, meditation and muscle relaxation. All have been proven to help people with anxiety – and they make you feel good.

Anxiety is not your eternal destiny and you don't need to be a passive recipient. Taking charge of the mind may seem hard. But you have the power to choose your thoughts. You have the power to be kind to yourself. Learning how to recognise and modify the thought processes underlying anxiety is a skill – one you can learn and with practice become very good at. These mind and body skills are incredible weapons in the fight against anxiety.

You are not alone. And seeking the support of others, whether professionals, friends, family members or others in the community is vital. By reaching out, you are doing the most important thing – supporting yourself.

In the day-to-day there are small things you can do to make a big difference to getting on with life, whether it's planning how to exit social engagements, creating art or rediscovering play, managing your finances or managing conflict. And, most importantly, remembering to live in the moment and to breathe.

Anxiety may be here but it does not need to stay. It is a visitor on your life's journey, and with the help of this book you may be able to bid it farewell as you regain the reigns of your life. You can do it.

Here you will find a willing hand to guide you through the mental challenges, tricks and deceits of old mate, Anxiety, and help you find a better path.

understand
anxiety

'Not all storms come
to disrupt your life;
some come to clear your path.'

ANON

understand anxiety

Everyone feels anxious now and then, usually when the situation (a speech, a date, a first day in a new job, for instance) calls for it. And that's fine and normal. But when these feelings endure beyond the event and start to manifest in the body, anxiety may have taken hold. The term 'anxiety' relates to a group of disorders such as phobias, panic attacks, obsessive behaviour and what's known as generalised anxiety disorder (GAD). This type of anxiety is characterised by excessive worry about everyday matters for no obvious reason and affects many people.

don't tell yourself it's helping

Some people with GAD believe that worrying might help control a perceived negative event, resulting in a better outcome, thereby convincing themselves that worrying is somehow helpful. But it's not. Such positive beliefs about worry quickly lead to anxiety and help maintain its status as top dog in your life. If you're telling yourself that it's helping, then stop. It's not.

understand worry

Worry, worry, worry. It's the persistent, horrible, niggling feeling at the heart of GAD. Scientists have sought to describe its key features and have determined that worry is often an uncontrollable stream of ideas that are concerned with future events (and possible disasters), which provoke feelings of apprehension (and other sensations in the body), which interfere with the ability to think clearly.

think about today

'Worrying is carrying tomorrow's load with today's strength – carrying two days at once. It is moving into tomorrow ahead of time. Worrying doesn't empty tomorrow of its sorrow, it empties today of its strength.'

CORRIE TEN BOOM

don't make worry the boss

'Don't let your mind bully your body into believing it must carry the burden of its worries.'

TERRI GUILLEMETS

don't believe your worries

'Stress is an ignorant state. It believes everything is an emergency.'

NATALIE GOLDBERG

understand the body's reaction

The body is hardwired to respond to perceived threats, like attack by a wild animal. The mind becomes alert, on edge. Heart rate speeds up, blood pressure rises. Sweat helps cool the body. Bodily functions such as digestion, the production of saliva and immune system responses slow down to conserve energy. Breathing becomes fast and shallow, increasing oxygen available to the muscles, perhaps causing palpitations or dizziness. The bladder and anus relax, creating the urge to go to the toilet. Pupils dilate, letting in light to help you see better in the cave. Is it any wonder we don't feel great when these responses are activated in the absence of a 'real' threat?

'The great thing, then, in all education, is to make our nervous system our ally instead of our enemy.'

WILLIAM JAMES

see it, don't fear it

Anxiety is a normal reaction. The changes in the body and in the way we think and behave enable us to deal with danger. This can be very useful if you need to get out of the way of a fast-moving car or escape another dangerous situation. Take a moment to acknowledge the wonder of your body and its constant willingness to fight for you. Try not to fear these changes in the body, and know that your body simply wants the best for you. Your job is to train your mind to follow suit.

moderate, don't try to eliminate

Take the middle ground. Anxiety is hardwired, and at times a useful response, so you will never banish it from your life altogether. But you can learn to manage and control it, and that's the good news you need to know and believe in.

give yourself credit

Anxiety won't help you solve a problem, but on the plus side it probably means you are a nice person. Most often anxiety strikes in sensitive, kind people who have a gift for empathy and understanding others. This may mean people warm to you. It probably also means that you are thoughtful and act with integrity towards others. Give yourself credit for this.

get to know yourself

It's helpful to dig deep and explore
what lies beyond the accessible level
of our personality and conscious
thoughts. You could start by reflecting
on your assumptions and core beliefs.
Assumptions are rules we have made that
we inadvertently live our lives by, such
as 'If I disagree with a friend, she will no
longer like me'. Core beliefs are absolute
statements you make about yourself and
your world, such as 'I am inadequate or
unlovable'. They reflect the very essence
of us. If these beliefs and assumptions are
negative, you're off to a bad start. Now
is the time to rethink. Don't you deserve
better?

look for themes

It's easy to take your thoughts for granted and let them run unchecked in your mind, so much so that it might not even have occurred to you to have identified a thought or thought pattern as negative. Look for themes in your thoughts. Do you tend to create unsolvable problems, do you blame others, do you assume the worst? Be vigilant with yourself, searching for and noting these kinds of patterns.

keep an anxiety diary

Keep a daily log of your anxiety, noting when it's at its best and worst, and try to make connections with what's happening in your life at those times. Note any situations you avoid due to anxiety and any behaviours that you don't like in response to it. This will help you identify triggers and in the long term help you proactively manage your anxiety.

accept your past

'Whatever happens to you belongs to you. Make it yours. Feed it to yourself even if it feels impossible to swallow. Let it nurture you because it will.'

CHERYL STRAYED

believe in yourself

'Staying positive does not mean that things will turn out okay. Rather it is knowing that you will be okay no matter how things turn out.'

ANON

stop
checking

People with anxiety are notorious
checkers. Whether it's checking in with
family to see that they are still alive or
triple-checking an important email or
report for work before sending it, anxiety
lurks in the driver's seat of this behaviour.
When you relentlessly pursue perfection,
you lose the chance to build trust and
enjoy back-and-forth relationships,
which are built on the assumption that
things go right sometimes and wrong
sometimes. So check-in and check over
mindfully. Do you really need to? What
will happen if you don't?

learn about your anxiety

Mental-health problems are less shrouded in secrecy than they used to be – a lot less. So step up and take advantage of all the resources that exist to educate and support you in your struggle with anxiety. Speak to professionals and other people similarly affected, read books and relevant websites, connect on social media. The more you can learn, the more tools and support you will have available to help you get through to the other side of your anxiety. You got this.

know
that it's not
your fault

'Feelings don't try to kill you, even
the painful ones. Anxiety is a feeling
grown too large. A feeling grown
aggressive and dangerous. You're
responsible for its consequences, you're
responsible for treating it. But... you're
not responsible for causing it. You're
not morally at fault for it. No more
than you would be for a tumor.'

PATRICK NESS

let yourself off the hook

Some days are just tough. Maybe today was that day for you. Perhaps you had a panic attack, leaving you feeling shaken and ashamed. Be kind to yourself. Acknowledge that anxiety is a disease and you are doing your best to manage it. You are not alone.

challenge your mind

'You don't have to control your thoughts. You just have to stop letting them control you.'

DAN MILLMAN

don't rehearse tragedy

Make no mistake about it, how you think affects how you feel. Anxiety can lead you to assume the worst and obsess about it, imagining all kinds of disasters ahead. Don't let anxiety get away with treating you like this. You're going to need put in time and effort to keep on top of your monkey mind. Keep searching for the truth – what's real and what's just your anxiety talking – and be as objective as you can. The goal is not to change anything external or make anything better but simply to recognise when your thoughts are not helping and not reflecting reality.

come back to yourself

'It's always worth it to take a moment to acknowledge your difficulties, to find little pieces of gratitude, and to make your way back to your center.'

NANEA HOFFMAN

avoid
avoiding

Avoiding what makes you anxious is a
quick fix, but with short-term relief comes
long-term fear and worsened anxiety.
Confronting it is the long game, scary at
first, but little by little you conquer your
fears and the cloak of anxiety starts to lift
because you have learnt that what you
fear is unlikely to happen. And if it does?
You can cope. You are in control. Each
time you do this, you lessen the power of
your anxiety.

'It's OKAY to be scared. Being scared means you're about to do something really, really brave.'

MANDY HALE

be the bus driver

Give your negative thoughts a personality. Imagine what they are wearing and the colour of their hair. Imagine their name, voice and personality. Imagine yourself as the bus driver. Now tell that person to get off your bus.

cut yourself some slack

Give yourself a break. If something doesn't go how you wanted it to, however big or small, try accepting it with as much objectivity and fortitude as you can muster. For example, if you didn't get a job you applied for, instead of thinking of it as a personal failure try acknowledging your disappointment, accepting there is usually a good, objective reason, and be confident in your ability to cope.

choose the best thoughts

Ask yourself what are the pros and cons of thinking in this way and if there is another way to think, consider its pros and cons too – then simply choose the thought process that offers you the most advantages. And stick with it. If the mind tries to draw you back to the consideration of the issues, tell it that you have made a decision and further input is not required. Repeat as necessary.

'The greatest weapon against stress is our ability to choose one thought over another.'

WILLIAM JAMES

don't practise failure

'Anxiety is practicing failure in advance. Anxiety is needless and imaginary. It's fear about fear, fear that means nothing.'

SETH GODIN

stem
the flow

'Anxiety is a thin stream of fear trickling through the mind. If encouraged, it cuts a channel into which all other thoughts are drained.'

ARTHUR SOMERS ROCHE

never
say never

Beware of words like 'never', 'ever', 'nothing' and 'no one', particularly when preceded by 'I will', 'I won't', 'I can' or 'I can't'.

Things are rarely that clear-cut. Truly.

don't borrow trouble

Anxious people have a tendency to personalise things that, in truth, are nothing to do with them. Jane lost her job, so my job is under threat. A local woman my age has cancer. I could have cancer. That kind of thinking is totally pointless. Try empathy or finding practical ways to help people instead.

disrupt your thoughts

Be your own personal agitator, policing your inner voice and calling it out. Question yourself ruthlessly. Ask yourself: is this (negative) thought the only one I could have? Would this thought be accepted by others, by someone who loves me? Am I jumping to conclusions or is there a more objective way I can look at this issue?

beware perfection

'The perfect is the enemy of the good.'

ANON

make mistakes

It's often said that we learn from mistakes. It's now scientific fact. In 2011 psychologist Jason Moser discovered that when we make a mistake, synapses fire causing the brain to 'spark and grow'. Think of it like this. Mistakes are like a good friend – they come around often and are good for you. Perfection on the other hand is fickle, unreliable, almost never shows up and makes you feel bad. Not the kind of friend you want or need.

be a
bit crap

'I just give myself permission to suck.
I find this hugely liberating.'

JOHN GREEN

don't be a worry tree

'That the birds of worry and care fly over your head, this you cannot change, but that they build nests in your hair, this you can prevent.'

CHINESE PROVERB

don't worry about the worry

'Don't think and worry, nothing will happen. You may worry a million times – worry makes you worry more. Worry is an ingrown self-conflicting process of life which is endless. If it is true that the Creator of this creation takes care of everything – if this is true, then where is the worry?'

YOGI BHAJAN

reset your perspective

In the midst of a crisis – real or imagined – it can be useful to stop and ask yourself the simple question. 'Will this matter a year, or five years, from now?' It's a simple technique to reset the mind's perspective from the perceived problem of the moment to the context of our full lives. Normally the problem we are obsessing over is small fry when you look at it that way, and it's much easier to dismiss it or reframe it as something minor.

'If you treat every situation as a life and death matter, you'll die a lot of times.'

DEAN SMITH

tackle reality

Anxiety can make us fret and fret about
the way things ought to be. There's no
place for woulda, coulda, shoulda in your
life. Concentrate on dealing with things
as they are.

be still

'Stop a minute, right where you are. Relax your shoulders, shake your head and spine like a dog shaking off cold water. Tell that imperious voice in your head to be still.'

BARBARA KINGSOLVER

don't be passive

Pessimism and feelings of powerlessness love to hold hands with anxiety. And no, it ain't cute. It's destructive. If you feel you can do nothing to change a situation or you can't change the way you think, then listen carefully: you can and you must. Are you trying to find solutions, and are you committed to the goal of changing your thought patterns and thus your feelings? Do you feel it is achievable? Recommit. This is your life and you don't need to be a passive observer.

strand
strong

'Trust yourself. You've survived a lot, and you'll survive whatever is coming.'

ROBERT TEW

choose a better story

One of anxiety's greatest hobbies is predicting the future. Anxiety is great at this. It tells you all the terrible things that may, probably will, happen to you, and it warns you again and again not to do certain things because once upon a time that didn't work out well for you. Guess what, it's just a story that your anxiety is telling you to keep you close. Decide not to listen and opt for a better story instead. You have just opened yourself up to the possibility of change.

'You're worried about what-ifs. Well, what if you stopped worrying?'

SHANNON CELEBI

dismiss the worry (if it's imagined)

Think objectively about the thing you are worrying about and ask yourself if it is really likely to happen or not. The chance is not. So dismiss the worry. Speak out loud the words 'I don't know this for sure. This is a worry, which serves me no purpose. I acknowledge and dismiss this worry from my thoughts. I choose to focus on something that will serve me better' (or a version of this you prefer).

accept the worry (if it's real)

If on analysis you are left with the objective belief that your worry has basis, then ask yourself if there is anything you can do about it right now. If there is, then obviously do that. If not, then see if you can accept the worry and let it go. Speak out loud the words 'There is nothing I can do about this right now. I choose to accept the worry and focus on something else. I know that I can deal with it when the time is right.'

tune in

It's easy sometimes to become overwhelmed by feelings and to focus on them as the problem. If you think about it, the opposite is true. Our feelings are messengers, alerting us to the problem, which is usually something in our environment or circumstances. Likewise, stay attuned to your behaviour. Are you acting in ways you don't like? Then there may be a problem somewhere that you need to identify and try to fix.

check your reactions

'Every time you are tempted to react in the same old way, ask if you want to be a prisoner of the past or a pioneer of the future.'

DEEPAK CHOPRA

ask yourself if the worry is worth it

'Of all your troubles, great and small,
the greatest are the ones that don't
happen at all.'

THOMAS CARLYLE

try not to speculate

'It ain't no use putting up your umbrella till it rains!'

ALICE CALDWELL RICE

learn to problem solve

Problem solving can be thought of as 'helpful worry'. Here's what you do.

Write down the main problem. Be as specific as you can. Try to keep it focussed on you, so rather than 'My boss is horrible', say 'I am feeling undermined at work'.

Brainstorm all the possible solutions, good or bad, and then consider each solution in practical terms.

Choose the most practical solution.

Create a plan for how you can implement that solution.

Do it and review it regularly to check it is working.

don't lose valuable time

'Worry a little bit every day and in a lifetime you will lose a couple of years. If something is wrong, fix it if you can. But train yourself not to worry. Worry never fixes anything.'

MARY HEMINGWAY

make a decision

Indecision is another of anxiety's favourite tricks. Anxiety loves nothing more than to turn over options on an endless loop. Indecision, like procrastination, is simply avoidance. Labouring over a decision is usually far worse than any potential outcome of a decision. Ask yourself if there is really a right or wrong choice to be made, what would happen if you made the other decision, and, perhaps most importantly, what evidence is there that you are unable to make a decision.

'In a moment of decision,
the best thing you can do
is the right thing to do, the
next best thing is the wrong
thing, and the worst thing
you can do is nothing.'

THEODORE ROOSEVELT

allocate time to worry

Do you 'enjoy' worrying? That sounds crazy doesn't it? But why would you do it if it wasn't giving you some kind of satisfaction? It's pouring fuel into anxiety's open funnel. But you can choose to open or close that funnel whenever you want to. Try setting aside a time each day to worry. Make yourself comfortable, set a timer for 10 minutes and go for it. Worry as much as you can. When the timer goes off, stop and move onto something else. Did anything change from your dedicated worrying, did the feared consequence eventuate? Over time, through this practice you might learn to set aside your worrying and not bother coming back to it.

learn, practise and commit

Getting on top of your thoughts, and your anxiety, is not easy. It requires you to learn new skills and practise them regularly, and you are doing this against the wishes of your mate, anxiety. But the more you try, the greater the reward. Change will not be immediate, some days will be harder than others, sometimes progress will be at a snail's pace, or not at all, but it will come. Remember it is not how bad your anxiety is nor how long you've had it for that matters, but your commitment. That's the single most important factor in helping you ditch anxiety and choose better friends.

avoid negativity

'Try to say nothing negative about anybody for three days, for forty-five days, for three months. See what happens to your life.'

YOKO ONO

PS. Include yourself.

take things one at a time

'You don't have to see the whole staircase, just take the first step.'

MARTIN LUTHER KING

focus on something else

In moments of acute worry when you just can't seem to stop anxiety from doing its work, very deliberately choose to do something else. Disconnect from technology, particularly if there is a message or post that's bothering you. Give yourself a task, such as to make a phone call or begin the next job on the To Do list. If you can tick something off there, then all the better. Or do a jigsaw, read a book, wash the car or do some exercise. Like all mental challenges, this takes practice. Few people succeed in distracting themselves from the tyranny of anxious thoughts the first, second or even third time they try this. Keep doing it and success will come.

don't give up

'Hey you, keep living. It won't always be this overwhelming.'

JACQUELINE WHITNEY

accept setbacks

'One small crack does not mean that you are broken, it means that you were put to the test and you didn't fall apart.'

LINDA POINDEXTER

'Every setback is a
set up for a comeback.'

ANON

seek peace

'Peace is the result of retraining your
mind to process life as it is, rather than as
you think it should be.'

WAYNE W. DYER

stick with it

'You have dug your soul out of the dark, you have fought to be here; do not go back to what buried you.'

BIANCA SPARACINO

regulate
your body

'An anxious mind
cannot exist
in a relaxed body.'

EDMUND JACOBSON

free your feelings

Research suggests that worry acts as a proxy for emotional processing – meaning that your anxiety may be covering up buried emotions, whether consciously or unconsciously. Using the techniques of relaxation and mindfulness, you can learn to identify and free these stuck emotions, thus reducing your 'need' for anxiety.

be patient

'Your mind will answer most questions if you learn to relax and wait for the answer.'

WILLIAM S. BURROUGHS

explore mindfulness meditation

It sounds simple: sit comfortably, focus on the breath, and then bring your mind's attention to the present without drifting into concerns about the past or future. But of course that's pretty hard in reality. It takes practice and more practice. The reward – as proven by many a scientific study – is an easing of psychological stresses such as anxiety, depression and pain. As a first step consider using a guided meditation, or join a group which can provide additional motivation if needed.

'You have to have full
control of your mind,
and your mind has to know
you, and you have to know
your mind, and for that,
there is meditation.'

YOGI BHAJAN

learn a mindful mantra

'Breathing in, I calm my body. Breathing out, I smile. Dwelling in the present moment, I know this is a wonderful moment.'

THICH NHAT HANH

check your breathing

Set your timer for one minute. Breathe normally and count your breaths (one breath in and out is counted as one breath). Write down your score and take note if it is over 15 breaths per minute. If that's the case you need to work on reducing it. On average a person needs to take only 10 to 12 breaths per minute. More than that and it becomes easy to hyperventilate, which is common among anxiety sufferers. Practise breathing from the belly and out through the nose in a smooth, easy way.

learn to breathe slowly

Stand or sit quietly. Take a normal breath and hold it. Count to six then breathe out and in your mind say the word 'relax' as you exhale.

Breathe in for three seconds, then breathe out for three seconds, repeating the word 'relax' on each exhale. At this pace, you will take 10 breaths per minute.

At the end of the minute, take another normal breath and hold for six seconds. Then repeat the exercise.

Practise this slow breathing technique for five minutes at a time, four times a day. Or use it in a tricky situation that triggers your anxiety.

'Sometimes the most important thing in a whole day is the rest taken between two deep breaths.'

ETTY HILLESUM

do 15 minutes of yoga daily

'Move your joints every day. You have to find your own tricks. Bury your mind deep in your heart, and watch the body move by itself.'

SRI DHARMA MITTRA

try yin yoga

This form of yoga focusses on holding poses for a long time. The poses are passive – you don't engage muscles, just let gravity do its work. If that makes it sound easy, don't be fooled. It's in the 'sitting with' the stretch and the discomfort (not pain) that we get relief from the mind. Anxiety can do scary things to the body and bodily sensations, and it is natural to get upset and worried about that. Through the practice of yin yoga, we can learn not to run away from feelings of discomfort but to stay with them and observe. This process of observation, just as with confronting behaviours and thoughts associated with anxiety, helps dilute them.

relax your muscles

We naturally tense our muscles to perform everyday tasks in a competent and alert manner. The problem is that we fail to 'switch off' these muscles, which then becomes wired to tension and fail to notice its presence or, more importantly, the absence of its counterpart, relaxation. This tension can cause physical problems, such as headaches or back pain, as well as feelings of jumpiness and anxiety. So it is very important to learn to relax our bodies. By relaxing our bodies, we regain control over our minds and can better deal with anxiety.

practise daily

Common among anxiety sufferers, muscle tension is probably the most obvious physical symptom of anxiety. This exercise, practised regularly, can help ease the pain and discomfort. Sit in a comfortable chair. Close your eyes and then slowly tense and relax each major muscle group. Hold the tension as tightly as you can (don't worry if you get a little shaky) for 10 seconds per muscle group. Release for six seconds, noting the feeling of tension leaving the body. Concentrate on the difference in how your muscles feel before and after – this is key to the exercise. This progressive muscle relaxation technique has been shown to help people with anxiety.

don't be frightened of tension

As a rule, we use more muscles than we need to for everyday tasks such as sitting, standing, using a computer or driving. Muscle relaxation exercises should help reveal this to you. On the other hand, tensing muscles when needed to try to achieve something physical (that winning ace on the tennis court) or to brace for a challenging situation is perfectly normal. Don't be fearful of this type of muscle tension.

trust in your body

'I am reminded of the advice of my neighbor. "Never worry about your heart till it stops beating."'

E. B. WHITE

practise in public

The key to success in muscle relaxation is practising regularly, so it's good to have a couple of clandestine exercises up your sleeve that you can practise when you are out and about. This one just requires you to be seated. Take a small breath and hold it for seven seconds. At the same time, cross your feet at the ankles and press down hard with the upper calf while trying to lift the lower leg. Exhale and let go of the tension, say the word 'relax' to yourself and feel the muscles follow your instruction.

relax the shoulders and neck

We carry so much tension here. Try this simple exercise several times a day if you can. Set a timer on your phone to remind you. Hunch the shoulders up toward the head, then let the shoulders fall and arms hang down by your sides. Repeat a few times until you feel the tension ease. Use this technique whenever you need a 'quick fix' in a moment of tension.

develop the habit

Learning to relax is a skill that takes time and requires regular practice. This can be a bitter pill to swallow for anxiety sufferers who are characteristically impatient and naturally keen to find solutions to their problem. Persistence is important though, and writing off relaxation because it hasn't worked is likely the anxiety talking – because anxiety thrives on tension and would much prefer you to revert to your old ways. Don't let anxiety win. Set goals and commit to them.

get a massage

Massage therapists are experts at releasing the knots of tension that build up in our bodies and pushing them out, helping to ease tension and stress. But massage has other benefits too. It helps people connect and use touch to create an emotional link, promoting empathy, care and love. The environment too can help ease stress, with gentle music, smells and decor that evoke a sense of calm. Unless you have a regular person whom you know and trust for this kind of relaxing massage, look out for a practitioner accredited in Massage Therapy Practice.

have a hot bath

'There must be quite a few things that a hot bath won't cure, but I don't know many of them.'

SYLVIA PLATH

find your great surge

Great Surge is one of the best for reducing stress and anxiety, while the Gushing Spring will help you maintain health and promote longevity. Have you guessed what these are? Acupressure points based on traditional Chinese medicine. A little bit of research will direct you where on the body to find these points, and others, so that you can begin to experiment with applying pressure to them and seeing if it helps relieve your symptoms.

ground yourself

This simple but effective exercise helps interrupt your thought patterns, forcing you to shift your focus to the present moment and away from your anxieties. Try it whenever you need to escape your thoughts.

Name five things you can see in the room.
Name four things you can touch or feel.
Name three things you can hear.
Name two things you can smell.
Name one thing you can taste.

touch and describe an object

Locate an object close to you. Describe it as you would to someone who could not see it. Don't scrimp on any detail. Tell them its shape, colour, materials, patterns, function, size, defining features. Anything you can think of. Keep going until you feel calmer.

play the memory game

Declarative, or explicit, memory (the memory of facts and events) is a useful tool to deploy in moments of panic or anxiety. It helps to re-situate us in the present moment and the wider world. To calm your mind, challenge yourself to recite facts from your personal declarative memory (perhaps you know a lot about trees or chemical elements), or go for something simple – name as many animals as you can, name all the countries in the world, or count backwards from 100.

find your sound

The sound of a drum, gong, bell or sacred chant is commonly used for healing in ancient traditions. Through Buddhism and the wider practice of yoga, the idea of chanting mantras is becoming widespread. In meditation, the mantras 'Om' and 'So Hum' are used to shift focus away from the busy mind and back to our essential being, enabling connection with a universal consciousness. Practise chanting these mantras slowly out loud or in your head. If this is working for you, then explore this vast topic further as there are mantras available to suit specific intentions.

practise box breathing

Box (or square) breathing is a simple way to focus your attention on your breath and the present moment. There are variations on the method, but an easy visual way to do it is to use your finger to slowly trace the shape of a square in the air. On the first edge of the square, take a deep breath in, on the next line hold your breath for a second, on the third line breathe out slowly and on the final line hold your breath for a second. Repeat until you feel calmer.

listen to your beat

You'll be spoilt for choice for a metronome app, as musicians have driven demand for them, but all you need is something simple to help you track and tame your tempo. Racing thoughts and a racing heart are common features of anxiety, making for a fast natural counting pace. To calm the mind, sit in a quiet space and using the metronome app count to 100 several times, slowing your pace each time using the metronome. Keep practising with this, gradually reducing your pace and eventually finding your peaceful pace and going with it.

get support

'Healing takes time,
and asking for help
is a courageous step.'

MARISKA HARGITAY

get your doctor on board

Remember that anxiety is an illness, so it makes sense that your first port of call is your doctor. Some people feel silly going to the doctor with anxiety, as if it's making a trouble of nothing. But doctors are increasingly skilled in dealing with mental-health problems and can provide important referrals to specialists or free resources, which can sometimes be used under the supervision of your doctor. So talk to your doctor first and if she doesn't listen, find one who can help you.

get support online

Check out headtohealth.gov.au for great apps, forums and other resources to help you manage your anxiety.

To dig deeper, head to thiswayup.org.au, which offers online courses containing practical research-backed tools to help you understand and better cope with your anxiety. Among the courses available is the Generalized Anxiety Disorder course, which may prescribed by a doctor or completed without supervision and currently costs $59 for 90 days.

consider therapy

Cognitive behavioural therapy or CBT has been proven to help with anxiety. It's all about understanding the link between how you think (that's the cognition part) and how you act (or behave). This will shed light on the thought processes and patterns that are holding you back from beating anxiety. Once understood, these processes and patterns can be replaced by healthier ones and problem-solving thinking that will improve your coping skills. CBT can be undertaken in groups or one-to-one and treatment length can vary from a month to a year or more. Speak to your doctor about it as a first step.

try exposure therapy

This type of therapy can be really useful if you can pinpoint your anxiety to specific situations or experiences. You are guided by a therapist to face that situation in a safe environment without performing any of the rituals or avoidance tactics you usually resort to. This direct approach can be challenging to people with anxiety, but if you are able to push through it you are likely to learn that the thoughts and rituals you have created do not serve any real purpose, and so you will be free of them.

try dance therapy

Believe it or not something as beautiful as dance can be a defence against anxiety. It's thought to work in two ways. It pops a pin into the inflated balloon of our anxious thoughts, simply by making us focus on something else, and it helps integrate the physical, emotional and cognitive parts of ourselves through movement. Professional therapists know how to help you release tension and bring greater body awareness and integration. These amazing people can use your body's movements, just like another therapist might listen to your words, to assess how you are doing.

seek help together

Even if anxiety affects only one member directly, involving the whole family in the solution can be helpful. Everybody can benefit from the direct support and involvement of their loved ones, and the opportunity to build even more open and honest communication. Likewise if your relationship with a partner has come under strain, relationship therapy may help improve it.

consider social skills training

It's common for people with anxiety to fear social situations, but it's important to address this so that you can take part and receive all the benefits that come with social interaction. It might sound odd to learn how to 'talk' to people, but why not? Not everyone is good at it, and it's a skill like anything else. Social skills training teaches – or reminds – people how to act in various social situations, giving you a chance to practise in a safe environment.

re-think your story

The stories we tell about ourselves can come to define how we think about ourselves and who we are, and yet they are not necessarily 'true' – or, at least, we refine them over time, embellishing with our (perhaps negative) angles and interpretations. Thus our stories become lodged in the framework of how we think and the language we use to express how we think. Narrative exposure therapy helps us to edit and re-write these stories so that we are no longer a victim, or powerless, or unloved, meaning they are less likely to cause anxiety.

get needled

It's a strange thought that having little needles stuck into your body can relax you, but that's the truth. It's long been at the heart of ancient Chinese medicine, whose practitioners believe the practice shifts qi (energy), which moves through the body on meridians, or pathways. Western doctors believe acupuncture needles mobilise metabolism, jump-starting chemical reactions and the nervous system, helping the body to heal itself. Whatever the reason, it feels great and it's likely going to help you, so give it a go.

smell
the roses

There's nothing to lose because at the
very least you can enjoy the pleasing
aromas of essential oils. If you see an
aromatherapy practitioner they will create
a blend specially for you in the belief
(for which there is some evidence) that
the oils' properties will have therapeutic,
healing effects. They can be diluted in
carrier oils and rubbed onto the skin or
used in a diffuser.

look to the east

In Ayurveda, the ancient Indian form of healing, anxiety is seen to stem from an imbalance of 'vata dosha'. Vata is the air principle and too much of this light, dry energy causes erratic thoughts, worries and obsessions – too much energy in the mind and not enough at the feet. To treat this with an Ayurvedic approach, you have to stabilise your energy and connect your body to the earth. Ayurvedic medicine would prescribe activities, diet and herbal supplements to facilitate this. See a practitioner to find out more.

get the power of plants

In the early 20th century, British physician Dr Edward Bach devoted his life to the discovery of 38 remedies made from plants that correspond to 38 negative emotional states. His remedies are still in existence and widely available commercially. You could see a practitioner for a personal recommendation or research online. The remedies, which are claimed to contain small amounts of a plant's life force, address emotional imbalances by flooding negative emotions with the positive energy of the plants.

have a chamomile tea instead

This is no secret. Caffeine (from coffee, tea, Coke and chocolate) stimulates the nervous system. Drinking a lot of it can replicate symptoms of anxiety such as restlessness and nervousness. Have a calming chamomile tea (or other herbal tea) instead.

try tapping

Dubbed 'acupuncture without needles', this treatment involves tapping an acupuncture point that has been identified by the practitioner as a target for change. It's thought this shifts qi, or energy, helping to restore a disturbance in the body's electrical energy field.

eat enough magnesium

Magnesium is known for its calming effect on the nervous system as well as other benefits, and periods of stress can deplete our bodies of this essential mineral. Include plenty of leafy greens, nuts and seeds, bananas and grains in your diet.

take omega-3

Scientific studies have demonstrated a positive effect of omega-3 polyunsaturated fatty acids (PUFAs) on anxiety. Omega-3 oils are commonly found in fish such as salmon, mackerel and tuna and are also available in supplement form.

eat
regularly

Numerous studies have shown a link between anxiety and 'functional hypoglycaemia' – that is, all the symptoms of hypoglycaemia, such as depression, anxiety, insomnia, irritability, crying spells, forgetfulness, trembling, racing heart and dizziness, but without the drop in blood sugar to the official hypoglycaemic range. Huh? Put it this way: people with anxiety have a greater likelihood of being affected by blood sugar levels, which exacerbates their symptoms. To combat this, eat regularly and avoid too much sugar.

think
lifestyle
change

Anxiety is a complex problem and there are no quick or simple solutions. Because so many people suffer from it, there are what can appear to be a confounding array of possible 'cures'. The key to improvement may be to seek solutions in many dimensions of your life, not just a one-trick-one-time approach. And most certainly these activities should be practised with diligence and commitment if improvement is to be expected.

tell someone

It might be the last thing you feel like doing. Anxiety is a cruel companion and will try to trick, shame and guilt you out of getting the support you need. But don't be deceived. You are loved and your friends and family want to help you. They need to know when you are suffering. It might help to nominate a support person who is lined up and will understand when you message, text or call. That way you won't have to explain yourself anew each time. It sounds like a small thing – to have someone there for you when you are feeling desperate – but it's a huge thing in terms of warding off isolation, staying connected and not allowing your anxiety to get the upper hand.

learn from others

Talking with other people who also experience anxiety can help you feel less alone. Visit online forums or join a support group to connect with others. Appropriate groups can be found via your doctor, local community health centre, state-wide mental-health foundation, or online mental-health websites such as Beyond Blue (beyondblue.org.au).

download an app

Take your pick from one of hundreds of amazing apps to help you manage anxiety. With apps such as Headspace or Rootd or Calm you can do guided meditations, follow breathing exercises, track your progress and listen to nature sounds or sleep stories. Or try an app geared to a more specific activity such as Acupressure: Heal Yourself, or Stop Panic and Anxiety, which is designed for sufferers of panic attacks.

put your health first

'I promise you nothing is as chaotic as it seems. Nothing is worth diminishing your health. Nothing is worth poisoning yourself into stress, anxiety, and fear.'

STEVE MARABOLI

cry like a baby

'Crying, that is, sobbing is the earliest and deepest way to release tension. Infants can cry almost from the moment of birth, and do so easily following every stress that produces a state of tension in the body... Human beings are the only creatures who can react in this way to stress and tension. Most probably, they are the only ones who need this form of release.'

ALEXANDER LOWEN

'People cry, not because they are weak. It is because they've been strong for too long.'

JOHNNY DEPP

live your
life

'Life is tough,
my darling,
but so are you.'

STEPHANIE BENNETT-HENRY

get up

Lying in bed won't solve anything,
it won't calm the mind or stave off the
panic. So if you possibly can, get up.
Confront yourself. Move.

'No matter how you feel,
get up, dress up, show up
and never give up.'

REGINA BRETT

know your values

'Almost all stress, tension, anxiety, and frustration, both in life and in work, comes from doing one thing while you believe and value something completely different.'

BRIAN TRACY

create your affirmations

Develop a small number of personal affirmations (or a single one) that you can repeat to yourself when anxiety strikes. Write them down and keep them somewhere accessible. If you don't regularly carry a bag, you could write them as a note on your phone. Write some brief words that work for you, expressing the idea that you are safe, this feeling will pass, nothing bad is happening, you can cope, you are supported and loved. Look online for ideas if you are stuck.

stand tall

How we carry ourselves speaks volumes. Hunched shoulders tells others we are fearful, and it conveys a similar message within, as our brains interpret tense muscles as a sign of imminent danger. Numerous studies have shown that good posture is associated with greater confidence, improved energy and a reduction in symptoms associated with anxiety and depression. As your mum might have told you numerous times before, put your shoulders back and your head up. And relax your muscles every time it occurs to you to do so.

slow down

'For fast-acting relief, try slowing down.'

LILY TOMLIN

prepare for social situations

If social situations scare you (and let's face it they scare many of us) there are a few simple things you can do to help make it easier. The biggie is to plan your entry and your exit. For your 'entry', think timing (being late is stressful), clothing, and the logistics of getting there. Exiting can be more tricky, but it's important to have a plan. That means make sure you have a good excuse as well as practical arrangements in place, if needed, to leave whenever you want to. Small talk is hard for most of us, so try practising in advance. Little things such as eye contact, listening to others and not interrupting are good tips to bear in mind.

fake it if you need to

'To pretend to be calm is to be calm, in a way.'

GILLIAN FLYNN

look left and right

'Before you diagnose yourself with depression or low self esteem, first make sure you are not, in fact, just surrounded by assholes.'

NOTORIOUS D.E.B.

don't worry what people think

'You wouldn't worry so much about what others think of you if you realized how seldom they do.'

ELEANOR ROOSEVELT

manage personal triggers

You only get one life, so there's no point in wasting it worrying about certain people or things that provoke your anxiety. Know your triggers (use journaling, therapy, practising being honest with yourself) and manage them. That doesn't mean you need to avoid them altogether, but it does mean being mentally prepared for how you will deal with them, whether that's by use of breathing, affirmations or another technique you've learned.

look after yourself

'How we care for ourselves gives our brain messages that shape our self-worth so we must care for ourselves in every way, every day.'

SAM OWEN

don't take it on

'You can't keep blaming yourself.
Just blame yourself once, and move on.'

DAN CASTELLANETA

say no

'You can be a good person with a kind heart and still say No.'

ANON

manage your finances

Believe it or not, money anxiety disorder is an actual thing. Symptoms can range from refusing to open credit-card bills to binge spending, under-charging or giving away money, and avoiding conversations about it. Like most things, it stems from childhood experiences with money. The good news is that you can get help for this and turn the behaviour around. Even if you don't have a problem as such, taking control of your finances is grounding and an important step in taking control of your life. A good place to start is by reading *The Barefoot Investor*, which has associated Facebook groups offering good support.

celebrate every tiny victory

'We ourselves feel that what we are doing is just a drop in the ocean. But the ocean would be less because of that missing drop.'

MOTHER TERESA

learn how to manage conflict

Many people with anxiety are fearful of conflict. It seems to stir the demons. Suddenly everyone else is better and more deserving than we are. You don't have to go in guns a-blazing to negotiate conflict. It's simply a skill and getting professional support can really help you to learn how to remain calm, be objective, take baby steps and gain the confidence needed to stop worrying about being nice and start focussing on getting what you want, need and deserve.

take
responsibility

'People and things do not upset us.
Rather, we upset ourselves by believing
that they can upset us.'

ALBERT ELLIS

keep
the faith

'No matter how chaotic it is, wildflowers will still spring up in the middle of nowhere.'

SHERYL CROW

learn from a kid's approach

'A child can always teach an adult three things: to be happy for no reason, to always be busy with something, and to know how to demand with all his might that which he desires.'

PAULO COELHO

play

Can its importance be over-estimated? No,
it cannot. Play is where we are free to be
ourselves, make mistakes, dream big, act
silly, laugh and connect with others. As we
age we forget that driving urge kids have to
play ('Are you playing? Are you playing?')
as we rush to fit into the straightjacket of
adulthood. But play is where we can again
find freedom and a lightness of spirit.
Everyone secretly just wants to play, so
find your thing, create your own games
or activities and watch others get on your
bandwagon. Or to make it really simple,
next time you are catching up for coffee
with a friend, suggest that you do some craft
activity together, or go kick a ball in the park.

'A lack of play should
be treated like malnutrition:
it's a health risk to your
body and mind.'

STUART BROWN

whistle

Or hum or sing or laugh. When we
do these things our body comes into
balance. The jaw unclenches, the facial
muscles relax, the lower back and legs
feel lighter. It's hard to do though when
you're feeling locked into your thoughts,
hanging out with your mate, Anxiety.
Give him a leave pass and see what it's
like without him. Just try, a little hum,
a little whistle or song. Force it out and
keep going. Joy will have its way with you
eventually.

be kind
to yourself

'What we don't need in the midst of struggle is shame for being human.'

BRENÉ BROWN

let it out

How come we've made anger the villain when the real damage is done by bottling it up where it stagnates and can mutate into anxiety and depression. If you know you've got it in you, then try releasing your anger in a controlled way such as via a martial art, running, throwing rocks into a river or shouting at the top of your lungs in a large field. If you can't seem to tap into your anger, it may be deeply repressed. Therapy can help with this, as can mindfulness exercises that focus on visualising a person or event that you find problematic and repeating the words 'I am angry' and noticing the sensations in the body.

'Never in the history of calming down has anyone ever calmed down by being told to calm down.'

ANON

take a moment to meditate

'Meditation is the ultimate mobile device; you can use it anywhere, anytime, unobtrusively.'

SHARON SALZBERG

go with the flow

'When you want to flow, flow humbly like water and co-exist. Water doesn't say, "Hey you three drops go to that side, we five go this way." Live with the flow of the psyche and if you do not develop that psyche by your own, you will be suffering with anxiety which has no answer.'

YOGI BHAJAN

let it be

'Our anxiety does not come from
thinking about the future, but from
wanting to control it.'

KAHLIL GIBRAN

don't forget
to breathe

'If you want to conquer the anxiety of life,
live in the moment, live in the breath.'

AMIT RAY

do something

'Nothing diminishes anxiety faster than action.'

WALTER ANDERSON

do something different

'If you think adventure is dangerous,
try routine. It is lethal.'

PAULO COELHO

practise letting go

'When I let go of what I am, I become what I might be. When I let go of what I have, I receive what I need.'

TAO TE CHING

keep hold
of you

'When you're feeling anxious, remember
that you're still you. You are not your
anxiety.'

DEANNE REPICH

focus on today

'Remember, today is the tomorrow you worried about yesterday.'

DALE CARNEGIE

make space
for the new

'Knowledge is learning something
new every day. Wisdom is letting go of
something every day.'

ZEN PROVERB

listen to music

Marconi Union's 'Weightless' has been dubbed the 'world's most relaxing song' after it was the subject of a neurological study. Participants were given challenging (stress-inducing) puzzles to solve, and listening to this song resulted in a 65 per cent decrease in anxiety during the process. Music has long been used as a tool in medicine and has recently proven to be as effective as drugs in relaxing patients prior to surgery. Try listening to this song (or music of your choice) when you need to find a way to switch off and relax.

'Music has healing power.'

ELTON JOHN

make some art

'Instead of worrying about what you cannot control, shift your energy to what you can create.'

ROY BENNETT

'Anxiety is the hand maiden of creativity.'

T. S. ELIOT

understand the value of exercise

'The stress-response is about preparing your body for an explosive burst of energy consumption right now; psychological stress is about doing all the same things to your body for no physical reason whatsoever. Exercise finally provides your body with the outlet that it was preparing for.'

ROBERT M. SAPOLSKY

Keep going

'If you're going through hell, keep going.'

ANON

dance like a banshee

Go wild in the kitchen, spin like a whirling dervish, dress up in tea towels and croon into a wooden spoon. Sing at the top of your lungs. Children optional.

watch a movie with a friend

'A true friend is someone who thinks that you are a good egg even though he knows that you are slightly cracked.'

BERNARD MELTZER

go outside

'I go to nature to be soothed and healed,
and to have my senses put in order.'

JOHN BURROUGHS

'I took a walk in the woods and came out taller than the trees.'

HENRY DAVID THOREAU

focus on your loved ones

'We spend precious hours fearing the inevitable. It would be wise to use that time adoring our families, cherishing our friends and living our lives.'

MAYA ANGELOU

laugh

'How can a person deal with anxiety? You might try what one fellow did. He worried so much that he decided to hire someone to do his worrying for him. He found a man who agreed to be his hired worrier for a salary of $200,000 per year. After the man accepted the job, his first question to his boss was, "Where are you going to get $200,000 per year?" To which the man responded, "That's your worry."'

MAX LUCADO

live your life for you

'I no longer force things. What flows, flows. What crashes, crashes. I only have space and energy for the things that are meant for me.'

ANON

keep believing

'Difficult roads often lead to beautiful destinations. The best is yet to come.'

ZIG ZIGLAR

quotes by

Walter Anderson
Acclaimed American artist, illustrator and potter.

Maya Angelou
American poet, storyteller, civil rights activist and autobiographer, best known for her 1969 memoir, *I Know Why The Caged Bird Sings*.

Roy T. Bennett
Inspirational author of *The Light in the Heart*.

Stephanie Bennett-Henry
Contemporary American poet.

Yogi Bhajan
(Harbhajan Singh Khalsa)
Indian-American yogi and spiritual teacher who brought kundalini yoga to the US.

Corrie ten Boom
Dutch watchmaker and later writer, saved an estimated 800 Jews during the Holocaust by providing refuge in her home.

Regina Brett
American bestselling self-development author.

Stuart Brown
Doctor, psychiatrist, founder of the National Institute for Play and author.

Brené Brown
American author of five No. 1 *New York Times* bestselling books on personal development and courageous leadership.

William S. Burroughs
Leading figure in the beat generation, American author and visual artist.

John Burroughs
Early-20th-century American naturalist and essayist.

Thomas Carlyle
Highly influential Scottish writer and poet of the Victorian era.

Dale Carnegie
American pioneer in the field of self-improvement, and writer of the bestselling *How to Win Friends and Influence People*.

Dan Castellaneta
Award-winning American actor, comedian, screenwriter and voice actor. Best known as the voice of Homer Simpson.

Shannon Celebi
American author of speculative fiction.

Deepak Chopra
Leading figure in the New Age and alternative medicine movements, and prolific author.

Paulo Coelho
Brazilian lyricist and novelist, best known for *The Alchemist*.

Sheryl Crow
Acclaimed American singer, musician and songwriter.

Johnny Depp
Award-winning American actor, movie producer and musician.

Wayne W. Dyer
American self-help guru, prolific author, internationally renowned motivational speaker.

T. S. Eliot
American author and poet and 1948 winner of the Nobel Prize in Literature.

Albert Ellis
Influential American psychologist, important contributor to the ideas behind cognitive behavioural therapy and the founder of rational emotive behaviour therapy (REBT).

Gillian Flynn
American author, best known for *Gone Girl*.

Kahlil Gibran
Lebanese-American painter, poet and writer, best known for his book *The Prophet*.

Seth Godin
American author and entrepreneur specialising in marketing, advertising, business venturing and leadership.

Natalie Goldberg
American writer and teacher, specialist in Zen approaches to writing.

John Green
American author (known for *The Fault in Our Stars*) and YouTube content creator.

Terri Guillemets
American quotation anthologist at quotegarden.com.

Mandy Hale
Blogger turned author and pioneer of 'the single woman' social-media movement.

Mariska Hargitay
American actress best known for her role on the show *Law and Order*.

Mary Hemingway
American journalist and author (and wife to Ernest Hemingway).

Etty Hillesum
Dutch diarist and mystic who died in Auschwitz aged 29.

Nanea Hoffman
American author, creator, social-media personality and founder of the blog Sweatpants & Coffee.

Edmund Jacobson
American doctor and creator of progressive muscle relaxation and biofeedback.

William James
'The father of American psychology', the first to teach a psychology course in the US.

Elton John
Legendary British singer and songwriter.

Martin Luther King
American scholar, minister and leader of the US civil rights movement.

Barbara Kingsolver
American novelist, essayist and poet.

Max Lucado
Bestselling American author whose books have sold over 100 million copies across 54 languages worldwide.

Steve Maraboli
American motivational speaker, bestselling author and behavioural science academic.

Bernard Meltzer
American radio personality best known as the host of his advice call-in show *What's Your Problem?*

Dan Millman
American former champion athlete turned prolific personal development author.

Sri Dharma Mittra
Brazilian guru of modern yoga, founder and director of the Dharma Yoga Center in New York City, and creator of the Master Yoga Chart of 908 Postures.

Mother Teresa
(Mary Teresa Bojaxhiu, Saint Teresa of Calcutta)
Albanian-Indian Roman Catholic nun and missionary.

Patrick Ness
American young adult author, journalist and lecturer.

Notorious D.E.B.
A notorious tweeter @debihope.

Yoko Ono
Japanese-American conceptual and multimedia artist, singer, songwriter and peace activist.

Sam Owen
British relationships and life coach, psychologist, author, blogger, vlogger and media personality.

Sylvia Plath
Notorious and admired American poet, novelist and short story writer.

Linda Poindexter
Writer, humorist and cartoon captionist.

Amit Ray
Indian enlightened spiritual master in the Himalayan yoga and vipassana tradition, author and philosopher.

Deanne Repich
American anxiety educator, teacher and founder and director of the National Institute of Anxiety and Stress, Inc.

Alice Caldwell Rice
American novelist and writer of short stories for children.

Arthur Somers Roche
American author known for his books in the mystery genre.

Theodore Roosevelt
The 26th (and youngest at age 46) US president.

Eleanor Roosevelt
American political figure, human rights activist and author.

Sharon Salzberg
American teacher of Buddhist meditation practices in the West, co-founder of the Insight Meditation Society, and bestselling author.

Robert M. Sapolsky
American neuroendocrinologist, author and professor at Stanford University.

Dean Smith
American athlete and basketball 'coaching legend'.

Bianca Sparacino
Canadian writer.

Cheryl Strayed
American inspirational speaker, author and podcast host.

Tao Te Ching
Ancient Chinese text, based on principles of philosophical and religious Taoism, reputedly written by Lao Tzu.

Robert Tew
American writer.

Thich Nhat Hanh
Expatriate Vietnamese Zen Buddhist monk, teacher, author, peace activist and the father of 'engaged Buddhism'.

Henry David Thoreau
Nineteenth-century
American philosopher, poet,
and environmental scientist,
whose writing on social reform
influenced leaders worldwide.

Lily Tomlin
Legendary American comedian
and TV, film and stage actress.

Brian Tracy
American-Canadian self-
development guru, speaker
and author of over 70 books.

E. B. White
American children's author,
long-standing contributor to
The New Yorker and co-author
of *The Elements of Style.*

Jacqueline Whitney
Instagram poet and writer.

Zig Ziglar
American salesman turned
motivational speaker.

HERRON

First Published in 2020 by Herron Book Distributors Pty Ltd
14 Manton St
Morningside
QLD 4170
www.herronbooks.com

Custom book production by Captain Honey Pty Ltd
12 Station Street
Bangalow
NSW 2479
www.captainhoney.com.au

Text on pages 12, 13, 14, 18, 20, 21, 22, 23, 24, 25, 28, 29, 31, 34, 36, 38, 39, 40, 44, 45, 46, 48, 52, 54, 56, 58, 60, 61, 62, 66, 68, 70, 71, 74, 82, 84, 87, 88, 91, 92, 93, 94, 96, 97, 98, 99, 101, 102, 103, 104, 105, 106, 107, 110, 111, 112, 113, 114, 115, 116, 117, 118, 119, 120, 121, 122, 123, 124, 125, 126, 127, 128, 129, 130, 136, 139, 140, 142, 146, 150, 152, 156, 158, 160, 172, 178 copyright © Captain Honey Pty Ltd 2020

Cataloguing-in-Publication. A catalogue record for this book is available from the National Library of Australia

ISBN: 978-0-947163-70-9

Printed and bound in China

5 4 3 2 1   19 20 21 22 23